Max and Moritz

Max und Moritz

Max und Moritz

eine Bubengeschichte

in sieben Streichen

von

Wilhelm Busch.

Max and Moritz

A Story of Two Bad Boys in Seven Tricks

by
WILHELM BUSCH

Translated by
ANN ELIZABETH WILD

English and German

Edition Tintenfaß

© 2011 Edition Tintenfaß
69239 Neckarsteinach / Germany
Tel. / Fax: +49 - 62 29 - 23 22
www.verlag-tintenfass.de
info@verlag-tintenfass.de

Satz: OLD-Media, Heidelberg

Druck: Appel & Klinger, Schneckenlohe

ISBN 978-3-937467-94-8

Preface

Wilhelm Busch's *Max und Moritz*, rightly called a precursor of modern comic strips, or to use the more modern term "graphic novels," is a true classic among children's books. First published in Munich in 1865, the book has by now been translated into over fifty different languages and at least twice as many (mainly German and English) dialects. In German-speaking countries, every child knows the book, and many adults can recite parts of the stories by heart. With an English translation appearing in Boston as early as in 1870, America was among the first countries to grant the two rascals "immigrant status." Later, Rudolph Dirks "naturalized" them as "Hans and Fritz" in his ever popular comic strip *The Katzenjammer Kids*, soon to be followed by Lyonel Feininger's *Kin-der-Kids*, both modelled after Busch's famous story.

In Britain, the book made its first appearance in 1874 in an anonymous translation published in London. Since then, at least a dozen other English translations have been issued.

Ann Elizabeth Wild's *Max and Moritz* is a congenial new rendering into modern English of the "story of two bad boys in seven tricks." She not only succeeds in faithfully translating the original using Busch's favourite trochaic tetrameter, but also manages most convincingly to convey the author's sense of humour and wit, and to echo his mastery of language and skill of versification. We are pleased to publish her translation for the first time. Printing the German text next to the English will give readers fluent (or interested) in both languages the opportunity to compare Busch's famous original with Ann Wild's fine translation.

The translator was born in England, spent her childhood in New Zealand and Australia and returned to England to complete her degrees in chemistry and botany at the Universities of Exeter and Durham. She then worked for some years in scientific research. Since 1976 she has lived in Germany (Dortmund, Würzburg, Kulmbach, Freiburg) as a scientific translator. Her *Struwwelpeter* translation (*Scruffypete*) was published in 2002 by Bolchazy-Carducci Publishers, Mundelein, Illinois in *Shock-Headed Peter in Latin – English – German*. She is also the author of a book about bobbin lace (*Geklöppelte Kugeln – Bobbin Lace Balls*, 2006), lacemaking being her other principal passion, together with translating.

Walter Sauer

Foreword   Vorwort

Oh! How often tales of sly,   Ach, was muss man oft von bösen
Naughty children make us sigh.   Kindern hören oder lesen!
These two here played wicked games –   Wie zum Beispiel hier von diesen,

Max and Moritz were their names –   Welche Max und Moritz hießen;
And they had no time for learning,   Die, anstatt durch weise Lehren
Or for growing more discerning,   Sich zum Guten zu bekehren,
And advice to mend their ways   Oftmals noch darüber lachten
Had them sniggering for days.   Und sich heimlich lustig machten.
But for things they shouldn't do   Ja, zur Übeltätigkeit,
They had time enough, these two.   Ja, dazu ist man bereit!
Teasing, hurting man and beast,   Menschen necken, Tiere quälen,
Robbing fruit trees for a feast,   Äpfel, Birnen, Zwetschgen stehlen –
That is clearly much more fun,   Das ist freilich angenehmer
And, when all is said and done,   Und dazu auch viel bequemer,
Easier than church or school,   Als in Kirche oder Schule
Sitting still upon a stool.   Festzusitzen auf dem Stuhle.
But I have to say, "Oh dear!"   Aber wehe, wehe, wehe!
And I cannot stop a tear   Wenn ich auf das Ende sehe!
When I think of how the late   Ach, das war ein schlimmes Ding,
Max and Moritz met their fate.   Wie es Max und Moritz ging.
Therefore what they did, those two,   Drum ist hier, was sie getrieben,
Is here in this book for you.   Abgemalt und aufgeschrieben.

The First Trick

We find people here and there
Keeping hens with loving care,
Firstly for the egg a day
Which a hen is sure to lay,
Secondly as now and then
They enjoy a roasted hen;
Third, the feathers from this bird
Are by many folks preferred
In their quilts. It may be said,
No-one likes a chilly bed.

Erster Streich

Mancher gibt sich viele Müh
Mit dem lieben Federvieh;
Einesteils der Eier wegen,
Welche diese Vögel legen,
Zweitens: weil man dann und wann
Einen Braten essen kann;
Drittens aber nimmt man auch
Ihre Federn zum Gebrauch
In die Kissen und die Pfühle,
Denn man liegt nicht gerne kühle.

Widow Bolte – here you see her –
Truly does not like that either.

Seht, da ist die Witwe Bolte,
Die das auch nicht gerne wollte.

She keeps hens, in number three,	Ihrer Hühner waren drei
And a cock as well, you see.	Und ein stolzer Hahn dabei.
Max and Moritz find it clear	Max und Moritz dachten nun:
What they can get up to here.	Was ist hier jetzt wohl zu tun?
Quicker than these words are said	Ganz geschwinde, eins, zwei, drei,
They cut up a slice of bread,	Schneiden sie sich Brot entzwei,
Cut four pieces, quick as quick,	In vier Teile, jedes Stück
Each a little finger thick.	Wie ein kleiner Finger dick.
These they tie to bits of string	Diese binden sie an Fäden,
Crosswise. Four arms has the thing	Übers Kreuz, ein Stück an jeden,

| Placed in Widow Bolte's yard | Und verlegen sie genau |
| Where the cock is standing guard. | In den Hof der guten Frau. |

Once the bread has caught his eye,
He begins to crow and cry,
"Cock-a-doodle-doodle-doo!"
Till the hens come into view.

Kaum hat dies der Hahn gesehen,
Fängt er auch schon an zu krähen:
Kikeriki! Kikikerikih!!
Tak, tak, tak! – da kommen sie.

Cock and hens, they share the spread,
Gobble each a piece of bread.

Hahn und Hühner schlucken munter
Jedes ein Stück Brot hinunter;

Then they all become aware
None can move away from there,

Aber als sie sich besinnen,
Konnte keines recht von hinnen.

Right and left and stop and go,
Pull each other to and fro,

In die Kreuz und in die Quer
Reißen sie sich hin und her,

Flutter up into the air.
Oh my goodness! What a snare!

Flattern auf und in die Höh,
Ach herrje, herrjemine!

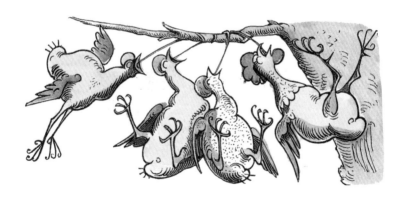

Woe! The string gets in a tangle
Round a branch and there they dangle.
And their necks grow long and longer
While their squawks sound wrong
and wronger

Ach, sie bleiben an dem langen
Dürren Ast des Baumes hangen.
Und ihr Hals wird lang und länger,
Ihr Gesang wird bang und bänger;

| And before their dying screech | Jedes legt noch schnell ein Ei, |
| One last egg is laid by each. | Und dann kommt der Tod herbei. |

| Widow Bolte where she lies | Witwe Bolte, in der Kammer, |
| Resting hears the awful cries, | Hört im Bette diesen Jammer; |

| Fears the worst and hurries out: | Ahnungsvoll tritt sie heraus: |
| Seeing puts an end to doubt. | Ach, was war das für ein Graus! |

From her eyes flow bitter tears.	»Fließet aus dem Aug, ihr Tränen!
"All my hopes and all my fears,	All mein Hoffen, all mein Sehnen,
All my dreams – now not to be –	Meines Lebens schönster Traum
Hang here on the apple tree!"	Hängt an diesem Apfelbaum!«

Deep distressed and full of care
With a knife she cuts the snare,
Cuts the bodies from the strings
So they need not hang, poor things.

Tief betrübt und sorgenschwer
Kriegt sie jetzt das Messer her;
Nimmt die Toten von den Strängen,
Dass sie so nicht länger hängen,

And in silent grievous pain
She goes back indoors again.

Und mit stummem Trauerblick
Kehrt sie in ihr Haus zurück.

That's trick one. Don't go away:
Number two comes straight away.

Dieses war der erste Streich,
Doch der zweite folgt sogleich.

The Second Trick

Once recovered from the shock,
Widow Bolte then took stock,
Thought that after due reflection
And sufficient circumspection
That although she was down-hearted
She would cook the dear departed,
Solemnly, with honour due,
And consume the chicken stew.
Clearly though, her grief was great
When the birds lay on the plate,
Naked without beak or feather –
They who once had scratched together
In the yard behind the cottage
Were to end their lives as pottage.

Zweiter Streich

Als die gute Witwe Bolte
Sich von ihrem Schmerz erholte,
Dachte sie so hin und her,
Dass es wohl das Beste wär,
Die Verstorbnen, die hienieden
Schon so frühe abgeschieden,
Ganz im Stillen und in Ehren
Gut gebraten zu verzehren.
Freilich war die Trauer groß,
Als sie nun so nackt und bloß
Abgerupft am Herde lagen,
Sie, die einst in schönen Tagen
Bald im Hofe, bald im Garten
Lebensfroh im Sande scharrten.

Widow Bolte stands there crying
And her spitz observes the frying.

Ach, Frau Bolte weint aufs Neu,
Und der Spitz steht auch dabei.

Max and Moritz smell the cooking.
In a trice the two are looking

Max und Moritz rochen dieses;
»Schnell aufs Dach gekrochen!« hieß es.

Down the chimney where they glimmer
Four fat chickens as they simmer,
Cleaned and headless, brown and hot,
Sizzling gently in the pot.

Durch den Schornstein mit Vergnügen
Sehen sie die Hühner liegen,
Die schon ohne Kopf und Gurgeln
Lieblich in der Pfanne schmurgeln.

Widow Bolte takes a platter,
And goes downstairs with a clatter.

Eben geht mit einem Teller
Witwe Bolte in den Keller,

From the barrel she doles out
One large portion sauerkraut,
Which she is most fond of when
It has been warmed up again.
In the meanwhile on the tiles
Two are practising their wiles.
Max, although it may seem odd,
Thought to bring a fishing rod.

Dass sie von dem Sauerkohle
Eine Portion sich hole,
Wofür sie besonders schwärmt,
Wenn er wieder aufgewärmt.
Unterdessen auf dem Dache
Ist man tätig bei der Sache.
Max hat schon mit Vorbedacht
Eine Angel mitgebracht.

Look! Hey presto! They are fishing   Schnupdiwup! Da wird nach oben
And one chicken is now missing.   Schon ein Huhn heraufgehoben.

Straight away the second rises
And the third now mobilizes.
Number four completes the haul.
"Great, for now we have you all!"
Spitz watched as the chickens went,
Yelped and barked his loud lament.

Schnupdiwup! Jetzt Numro zwei;
Schnupdiwup! Jetzt Numro drei;
Und jetzt kommt noch Numro vier:
Schnupdiwup! Dich haben wir!!
Zwar der Spitz sah es genau,
Und er bellt: Rawau! Rawau!

Max and Moritz are not slow,
Down and gone in half a mo'.
Oh, my goodness! Things look black:
Widow Bolte's coming back.
She stands rooted to the spot
As her glance falls on the pot.

Aber schon sind sie ganz munter
Fort und von dem Dach herunter.
Na! Das wird Spektakel geben,
Denn Frau Bolte kommt soeben;
Angewurzelt stand sie da,
Als sie nach der Pfanne sah.

| Not a single chicken left – | Alle Hühner waren fort, |
| Spitz can only look bereft. | »Spitz!« – das war ihr erstes Wort. |

| "Oh, you spitz, you wicked brat! | »Oh, du Spitz, du Ungetüm! |
| Just you wait, you'll pay for that!" | Aber wart! ich komme ihm!« |

With the ladle large and strong	Mit dem Löffel, groß und schwer,
Spitz is beaten hard and long;	Geht es über Spitzen her;
Loudly sound his cries of pain	Laut ertönt sein Wehgeschrei,
For he feels he's not to blame.	Denn er fühlt sich schuldenfrei.

Max and Moritz hide away,	Max und Moritz, im Verstecke,
Feast behind the hedge that day.	Schnarchen aber an der Hecke,
It was good, there is no doubt:	Und vom ganzen Hühnerschmaus
Just a drumstick's sticking out.	Guckt nur noch ein Bein heraus.
That's trick two. Don't go away:	Dieses war der zweite Streich,
Number three comes straight away.	Doch der dritte folgt sogleich.

The Third Trick Dritter Streich

In the village there's a man	Jedermann im Dorfe kannte
Known to all as Tailor Ramm.	Einen, der sich Böck benannte.

Trousers, tailcoats, coats for smokers,
Sunday best and fitting chokers,
Waistcoats made with proper plackets,
Gaiters, winter coats and jackets,
Tailor Ramm was good at making
Clothes for any undertaking.
And when something needed patching,
Cutting off or reattaching,
Buttons loose or buttons gone
From the trousers they were on,
Which whatever, whither, where,
Back or front or here or there,
Tailor Ramm will mend it too:
That is what he lives to do.
In the village every man
Wanted to be friends with Ramm.
But our Max and Moritz thought
Baiting Ramm could be good sport.

Alltagsröcke, Sonntagsröcke,
Lange Hosen, spitze Fräcke,
Westen mit bequemen Taschen,
Warme Mäntel und Gamaschen –
Alle diese Kleidungssachen
Wusste Schneider Böck zu machen.
Oder wäre was zu flicken,
Abzuschneiden, anzustücken,
Oder gar ein Knopf der Hose
Abgerissen oder lose –
Wie und wo und was es sei,
Hinten, vorne, einerlei –
Alles macht der Meister Böck,
Denn das ist sein Lebenszweck.
Drum so hat in der Gemeinde
Jedermann ihn gern zum Freunde.
Aber Max und Moritz dachten,
Wie sie ihn verdrießlich machten.

| There beside the tailor's door | Nämlich vor des Meisters Hause |
| Sounds a stream's incessant roar, | Floss ein Wasser mit Gebrause. |

| And the bridge is just a plank – | Übers Wasser führt ein Steg |
| So inviting for a prank! | Und darüber geht der Weg. |

Max and Moritz start once more,	Max und Moritz, gar nicht träge,
Saw in secret with a saw,	Sägen heimlich mit der Säge,
Saw and see and saw: those two	Ritzeratze! voller Tücke,
Cut the plank quite half-way through.	In die Brücke eine Lücke.

When the job is finished well,
Somewhere someone's heard to yell,

Als nun diese Tat vorbei,
Hört man plötzlich ein Geschrei:

"Hey, come out you silly Ramm,
Baa-baa baa-baa billy-lamb."
Many things good Ramm has heard,
And not said a single word;
This time when he hears that shout
Something in him turns about.

»He, heraus! du Ziegen-Böck!
Schneider, Schneider, meck, meck, meck!«
Alles konnte Böck ertragen,
Ohne nur ein Wort zu sagen;
Aber wenn er dies erfuhr,
Ging's ihm wider die Natur.

With the yardstick in his hand
In a flash he takes a stand.
Then he hears again from far,
"Billy-lamb, baa-baa baa-baa".

Schnelle springt er mit der Elle
Über seines Hauses Schwelle,
Denn schon wieder ihm zum Schreck
Tönt ein lautes: »Meck, meck, meck!«

| But the bridge takes just one shoe. | Und schon ist er auf der Brücke, |
| Crack! The plank has snapped in two. | Kracks! Die Brücke bricht in Stücke; |

| "Baa-baa-baa" the taunt goes on | Wieder tönt es: »Meck, meck, meck!« |
| Splash! And Tailor Ramm is gone. | Plumps! Da ist der Schneider weg! |

Ramm is sure that he must die.
But two geese come swimming by

Grad als dieses vorgekommen,
Kommt ein Gänsepaar geschwommen,

Which our Ramm in desperate fear
Grabs as soon as they are near.

Welches Böck in Todeshast
Krampfhaft bei den Beinen fasst.

Those two geese held in his hand
Flutter up onto the land.

Beide Gänse in der Hand,
Flattert er auf trocknes Land.

All of that, to be precise,
Ramm does not find very nice.

Übrigens bei alledem
Ist so etwas nicht bequem;

Even more when in its wake
He develops stomach-ache.

Wie denn Böck von der Geschichte
Auch das Magendrücken kriegte.

Here Ramm's wife is due high praise.
Her hot iron from the blaze
Placed on his cold body then
Puts it all to rights again.

Hoch ist hier Frau Böck zu preisen!
Denn ein heißes Bügeleisen,
Auf den kalten Leib gebracht,
Hat es wieder gut gemacht.

Soon you hear the village tell,
"Tailor Ramm is fit and well."

That's trick three. Don't go away:
Number four comes straight away.

Bald im Dorf hinauf, hinunter,
Hieß es: »Böck ist wieder munter!«

Dieses war der dritte Streich,
Doch der vierte folgt sogleich.

The Fourth Trick   Vierter Streich

As you know, there is a rule: Also lautet ein Beschluss:
Everyone must go to school.   Dass der Mensch was lernen muss.
But alone the ABC   Nicht allein das A-B-C
Does not make a person free.   Bringt den Menschen in die Höh;
Nor does just to write and read   Nicht allein im Schreiben, Lesen
Let a thinking man succeed.   Übt sich ein vernünftig Wesen;
Not alone for calculations   Nicht allein in Rechnungssachen
Should he practice permutations.   Soll der Mensch sich Mühe machen;
No, the wisdom of the wise   Sondern auch der Weisheit Lehren
He should learn to know and prize.   Muss man mit Vergnügen hören.

There to serve this worthy aim   Dass dies mit Verstand geschah,
Was a teacher, Lamp by name.   War Herr Lehrer Lämpel da.
Therefore Max and Moritz can   Max und Moritz, diese beiden,
Find no liking for the man,   Mochten ihn darum nicht leiden;
For the children who like fooling   Denn wer böse Streiche macht,
Do not take so well to schooling.   Gibt nicht auf den Lehrer Acht.

Mister Lamp, a good man clearly,
Cherished his tobacco dearly,
Which – beyond all question – may,
After a hard working day,
For a dear old man be bliss.
And we don't begrudge him this.
Max and Moritz did not lack
Schemes for launching an attack.
Here they planned a prototype
For our Lamp and with his pipe.
So it was on Sunday when
Mister Lamp in church again,

Nun war dieser brave Lehrer
Von dem Tabak ein Verehrer,
Was man ohne alle Frage
Nach des Tages Müh und Plage
Einem guten alten Mann
Auch von Herzen gönnen kann.
Max und Moritz, unverdrossen,
Sinnen aber schon auf Possen,
Ob vermittelst seiner Pfeifen
Dieser Mann nicht anzugreifen.
Einstens, als es Sonntag wieder
Und Herr Lämpel brav und bieder

Where this goodly worthy man
Played the organ with elan,

In der Kirche mit Gefühle
Saß vor seinem Orgelspiele,

That bad twosome, like a mouse,
Creeps into his empty house,
Finds his precious meerschaum there.
Max then holds it still with care

Schlichen sich die bösen Buben
In sein Haus und seine Stuben,
Wo die Meerschaumpfeife stand;
Max hält sie in seiner Hand;

While our Moritz has begun
With the powder for the gun,
Packs it deep into the bowl
Of the meerschaum, fills the whole.
Now the two must vanish quick:
Church is over in a tick.

Aber Moritz aus der Tasche
Zieht die Flintenpulverflasche,
Und geschwinde, stopf, stopf, stopf!
Pulver in den Pfeifenkopf.
Jetzt nur still und schnell nach Haus,
Denn schon ist die Kirche aus.

Mister Lamp felt deep content,
Locked the church before he went.

Eben schließt in sanfter Ruh
Lämpel seine Kirche zu;

| And with hymn book, psalter, score | Und mit Buch und Notenheften, |
| No official duties more, | Nach besorgten Amtsgeschäften, |

| Happily he set his feet | Lenkt er freudig seine Schritte |
| Homewards straight along the street, | Zu der heimatlichen Hütte, |

| Gladly filled his coffee cup, | Und voll Dankbarkeit sodann |
| Took his pipe and lit it up. | Zündet er sein Pfeifchen an. |

| "Ah!" says he, "Ah, life is good!" | »Ach!« – spricht er – »die größte Freud |
| "I'd not change it if I could!" | Ist doch die Zufriedenheit!« |

Bang! The pipe goes off. The boom	Rums! – Da geht die Pfeife los
Thunders round the little room.	Mit Getöse, schrecklich groß.
Pot and cup with coffee in,	Kaffeetopf und Wasserglas,
Inkwell and tobacco tin,	Tabaksdose, Tintenfass,
Stove and table, comfy chair:	Ofen, Tisch und Sorgensitz –
Everything flies through the air.	Alles fliegt im Pulverblitz.

When the smoke begins to rise	Als der Dampf sich nun erhob,
Dreadful prospects meet our eyes.	Sieht man Lämpel, der gottlob!
Mister Lamp, alive or dead?	Lebend auf dem Rücken liegt;
No, he's living, no blood shed,	Doch er hat was abgekriegt.

But his hands and face are quite	Nase, Hand, Gesicht und Ohren
Black as thunder, black as night,	Sind so schwarz als wie die Mohren,
Of his hair there's not a shred:	Und des Haares letzter Schopf
Burned off right down to his head.	Ist verbrannt bis auf den Kopf.

Now then who is going to teach
Children wisdom, spelling, speech?
"Who can undertake", one asks,
"Lamp's official daily tasks?"
And how can the teacher smoke
When his pipe is smashed and broke?

Wer soll nun die Kinder lehren
Und die Wissenschaft vermehren?
Wer soll nun für Lämpel leiten
Seine Amtestätigkeiten?
Woraus soll der Lehrer rauchen,
Wenn die Pfeife nicht zu brauchen?

Everything is healed in time.
Just the pipe has passed its prime.

That's trick four. Don't go away:
Number five comes straight away.

Mit der Zeit wird alles heil,
Nur die Pfeife hat ihr Teil.

Dieses war der vierte Streich,
Doch der fünfte folgt sogleich.

The Fifth Trick

In the town or country fair
He who has an uncle there
Should be always quite polite,
For an uncle finds that right.
And a bright "Good morning" he
Says and brings a cup of tea.
"Is there anything you need?
Pipe or paper, books to read?"
And when Uncle has an itch
Somewhere on his back and which
Can't be reached, his nephew then
Gladly comes to help again.
Or when Uncle's pinch of snuff
Tickles in his nose enough,
"Bless you!", follows on the sneeze,
"Thank you", and "Excuse me please!"
Or, when Uncle comes home late,
Pulls his boots off at the grate,
Brings him slippers, pipe and spill,
Dressing gown against the chill.
Simply, he should take good care
That his uncle's happy there.
Max and Moritz we shall find
Had quite other deeds in mind,
Put instead their wicked wits
Into teasing Uncle Fritz.

Fünfter Streich

Wer im Dorfe oder Stadt
Einen Onkel wohnen hat,
Der sei höflich und bescheiden,
Denn das mag der Onkel leiden.
Morgens sagt man: »Guten Morgen!
Haben Sie was zu besorgen?«
Bringt ihm, was er haben muss:
Zeitung, Pfeife, Fidibus.
Oder sollt es wo im Rücken
Drücken, beißen oder zwicken,
Gleich ist man mit Freudigkeit
Dienstbeflissen und bereit.
Oder sei's nach einer Prise,
Dass der Onkel heftig niese,
Ruft man »Prosit!« allsogleich,
»Danke, wohl bekomm es Euch!«
Oder kommt er spät nach Haus,
Zieht man ihm die Stiefel aus,
Holt Pantoffel, Schlafrock, Mütze,
Dass er nicht im Kalten sitze,
Kurz, man ist darauf bedacht,
Was dem Onkel Freude macht.
Max und Moritz ihrerseits
Fanden darin keinen Reiz.
Denkt euch nur, welch schlechten Witz
Machten sie mit Onkel Fritz!

Just what kind of bird a May-
 Bug could be we all can say.

Jeder weiß, was so ein Mai-
 Käfer für ein Vogel sei.

In the trees these creatures all
Fly about and creep and crawl.

In den Bäumen hin und her
Fliegt und kriecht und krabbelt er.

Max and Moritz on a spree
Shake the May-bugs from a tree.

Max und Moritz, immer munter,
Schütteln sie vom Baum herunter.

Into paper bags our thugs
Put the creepy crawly bugs.

In die Tüte von Papiere
Sperren sie die Krabbeltiere.

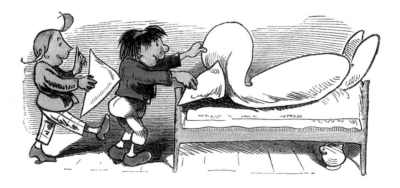

Quickly then those bugs are spilt
Under Uncle Fritz's quilt.

Fort damit und in die Ecke
Unter Onkel Fritzens Decke!

Uncle Fritz is soon in bed
With his nightcap on his head.
Eyes closed tight, he snuggles deep.
In a trice he is asleep.

Bald zu Bett geht Onkel Fritze
In der spitzen Zippelmütze;
Seine Augen macht er zu,
Hüllt sich ein und schläft in Ruh.

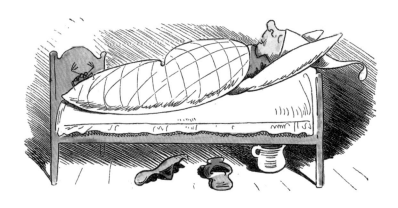

But the May-bugs in the bed
Creep along towards the head.

Doch die Käfer, kritze, kratze!
Kommen schnell aus der Matratze.

And the very first of those
Pinches Uncle Fritz's nose.

Schon fasst einer, der voran,
Onkel Fritzens Nase an.

"Ow!" he cries and "What is that?!!"
Apprehends the monstrous gnat.

»Bau!« schreit er – »Was ist das hier?«
Und erfasst das Ungetier.

Full of horror, shock and dread,
Uncle Fritz springs out of bed.

Und den Onkel, voller Grausen,
Sieht man aus dem Bette sausen.

"Ouch!" he feels them take a peck
At his foot, his leg, his neck.

»Autsch!« – Schon wieder hat er einen
Im Genicke, an den Beinen;

Everywhere he looks and leaps
Buzzes, scrabbles, crawls and creeps.

Hin und her und rund herum
Kriecht es, fliegt es mit Gebrumm.

Uncle Fritz in desperation
Stamps on, swats the infestation

Onkel Fritz, in dieser Not,
Haut und trampelt alles tot.

Till he's sure they all are dead
And he can go back to bed.

Guckste wohl! Jetzt ist's vorbei
Mit der Käferkrabbelei!

Uncle Fritz lies back and then
Shuts his eyes and sleeps again.

That's trick five. Don't go away:
Number six comes straight away.

Onkel Fritz hat wieder Ruh
Und macht seine Augen zu.

Dieses war der fünfte Streich,
Doch der sechste folgt sogleich.

The Sixth Trick

In the lovely Eastertide
When the bakers far and wide
All are busy while they bake
Hot cross buns and rolls and cake
Max and Moritz wished so much
For a taste of something such.

Sechster Streich

In der schönen Osterzeit,
Wenn die frommen Bäckersleut
Viele süße Zuckersachen
Backen und zurechte machen,
Wünschten Max und Moritz auch
Sich so etwas zum Gebrauch.

But the baker turned the key,
Wisely locked the bakery.

Doch der Bäcker, mit Bedacht,
Hat das Backhaus zugemacht.

So they try the chimney pot.
That's the only way they've got.

Also, will hier einer stehlen,
Muss er durch den Schlot sich quälen.

Now they're falling, heads then toes,
From the chimney, black as crows.

Ratsch! Da kommen die zwei Knaben
Durch den Schornstein, schwarz wie
Raben.

Our two scoundrels land within
In the box the flour is in.

Puff! Sie fallen in die Kist,
Wo das Mehl darinnen ist.

Look at them! For now they walk
Through the room, as white as chalk.

Da! Nun sind sie alle beide
Rund herum so weiß wie Kreide.

They see pretzels on the shelf.
Max climbs up to help himself.

Aber schon mit viel Vergnügen
Sehen sie die Brezeln liegen.

Crack! The chair is broken, so   Knacks! Da bricht der Stuhl entzwei;

See them landing in the dough.   Schwapp! Da liegen sie im Brei.

Wrapped in dough – oh, what a plight! –
Those two are a wretched sight.

Ganz von Kuchenteig umhüllt
Stehn sie da als Jammerbild.

But the baker comes back then,
Sees at once the yeast-bread men.

Gleich erscheint der Meister Bäcker
Und bemerkt die Zuckerlecker.

One, two three! Before you think,
Loaves are ready in a wink.

Eins, zwei, drei! – eh man's gedacht,
Sind zwei Brote draus gemacht.

And the oven is still hot.
Whoosh! He bakes them on the spot.

In dem Ofen glüht es noch –
Ruff! – damit ins Ofenloch!

| Whoosh! He draws them from the heat | Ruff! – Man zieht sie aus der Glut; |
| When the loaves are good to eat. | Denn nun sind sie braun und gut. |

| Are our Max and Mo' perdu? | Jeder denkt, die sind perdü! |
| No! They're still alive, those two, | Aber nein! – noch leben sie! |

Eat their way out like two mice:	Knusper, knasper! – wie zwei Mäuse
Fresh-baked bread tastes very nice!	Fressen sie durch das Gehäuse;

And the baker gives a shout,	Und der Meister Bäcker schrie:
"Goodness me! Those two got out!"	»Ach herrje! da laufen sie!«
That's trick six. Don't go away	Dieses war der sechste Streich,
For the last comes straight away.	Doch der letzte folgt sogleich.

The Last Trick   Letzter Streich

Max and Moritz, not so fast,   Max und Moritz, wehe euch!
For your next trick is your last!   Jetzt kommt euer letzter Streich!

Can you tell me why those brats   Wozu müssen auch die beiden
Have to cut holes in the sacks?   Löcher in die Säcke schneiden?

Farmer Leigh then lifts a great   Seht, da trägt der Bauer Mecke
Sack that weighs a hundredweight   Einen seiner Maltersäcke.

But he's hardly turned around,
Corn is pouring to the ground.

Aber kaum, dass er von hinnen,
Fängt das Korn schon an zu rinnen.

And he stops, says, "What a blighter!
This here sack is getting lighter!"

Und verwundert steht und spricht er:
»Zapperment! dat Ding werd lichter!«

"Ha!" For then he's glad to spy
Those two villains where they lie.

Hei! Da sieht er voller Freude
Max und Moritz im Getreide.

Quickly in his biggest sack
He then shovels that bad pack.

Rabs! – in seinen großen Sack
Schaufelt er das Lumpenpack.

Max and Moritz feel quite ill
For he's heading for the mill.

Max und Moritz wird es schwüle,
Denn nun geht es nach der Mühle.

"Mister Miller! Come here, do!
Quickly put this sackful through!"

»Meister Müller, he, heran!
Mahl er das, so schnell er kann!«

"Give it here!" And in the hopper
Those two rascals come a cropper.

»Her damit!« Und in den Trichter
Schüttelt er die Bösewichter.

Clatter, clatter, munch and crunch
Turns the mill with grinding scrunch.

Rickeracke! Rickeracke!
Geht die Mühle mit Geknacke.

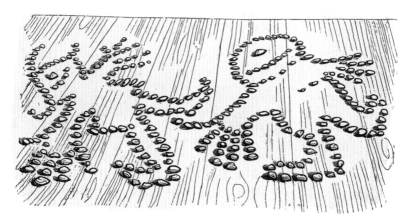

Here you see them when it ceases,
  Finely ground and all in pieces.

Hier kann man sie noch erblicken
  Fein geschroten und in Stücken.

Then a tasty meal they make

Doch sogleich verzehret sie

For the miller's duck and drake.

Meister Müllers Federvieh.

Ending

In the village all were glad,
Not a single soul was sad.
Widow Bolte's heard to say,
"So! I thought that straight away!"
Tailor Ramm exclaimed, "Oh, strife!
Malice is no way of life!"
Then good Mister Lamp replied,
"An Example they provide!"
And the baker spoke, "In truth,
What's the good of man's sweet tooth!"
Even gentle Uncle Fritz
Said, "That comes of ill-used wits."
While our stolid farmer Leigh
Thought, "All that is naught to me."
Through the village went around
Such a cheerful buzz of sound,
"Thanks to God! For now at last
All those wicked tricks are past!"

Schluss

Als man dies im Dorf erfuhr,
War von Trauer keine Spur.
Witwe Bolte, mild und weich,
Sprach: »Sieh da, ich dacht es gleich!«
»Ja, ja, ja!« rief Meister Böck,
»Bosheit ist kein Lebenszweck!«
Drauf so sprach Herr Lehrer Lämpel:
»Dies ist wieder ein Exempel!«
»Freilich!« meint der Zuckerbäcker,
»Warum ist der Mensch so lecker?!«
Selbst der gute Onkel Fritze
Sprach: »Das kommt von dumme Witze!«
Doch der brave Bauersmann
Dachte: »Wat geiht meck dat an?!«
Kurz, im ganzen Ort herum
Ging ein freudiges Gebrumm:
»Gott sei Dank! Nun ist's vorbei
Mit der Übeltäterei!«

Also available from Edition Tintenfass:

ISBN 978-3-937467-54-2

ISBN 978-3-937467-49-8

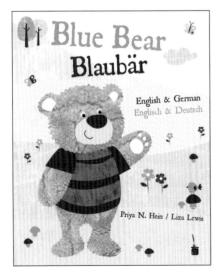

ISBN 978-3-943052-35-0

ISBN 978-3-937467-21-4

Edition Tintenfass, D-69239 Neckarsteinach, Tel. / Fax: +49 - 62 29 - 23 22
www.verlag-tintenfass.de / info@verlag-tintenfass.de